Little

Charles M. Schulz

ℛ
RAVETTE PUBLISHING

First published in 2001 by
Ravette Publishing Limited, Unit 3, Tristar Centre,
Star Road, Partridge Green, West Sussex RH13 8RA

Edited by Gordon Volke

Printed in Malta by Gutenberg Press

ISBN: 1 84161 100 X

Snoopy is the world-famous beagle and the cherished pet of Charlie Brown. He excels at sport (except the infuriating game of golf), lives for food and always attracts a crowd.

When Snoopy is not tracking down the nearest chocolate-chip cookie, he is engrossed in one of his many fantasies. Whether a clever lawyer, a great writer or a kindly Scoutmaster, Snoopy is the happy-go-lucky warm puppy everyone knows.

The special friendship between Snoopy and Woodstock began when a clutch of bird's eggs were hatched in a nest perched on Snoopy's stomach. Snoopy thought he'd never get rid of them because they couldn't learn to fly!

As time went on, one of the birds – Woodstock – became Snoopy's secretary and after-hours friend. Woodstock talks only in birdspeak which Snoopy translates. But they both speak a universal language with their relationship which delights millions!

When you're waiting for your supper, a watched back door never opens.

Those who believe in the "balance of nature" are those who don't get eaten.

You know it's cold when you can hear your feet coughing.

One of the great joys in life
is scoffing junk food!

Ten minutes before you
go to a party is no time
to be learning to dance!

Unfortunately, it's very hard
to forget someone
by drinking root beer!

To stay warm in winter,
insulate the ol' attic!

Necks hate to exercise.
If necks were feet,
you'd never go anywhere.

You can't discuss something with someone whose arguments are too narrow.

Feet are always mad
about something ...

A watched supper dish
never fills.

There's nothing more embarrassing than barking up the wrong tree!

Stocking caps are great ...
if you don't mind getting
your ears wrinkled.

My life is going by too fast ...
My only hope is that
we go into overtime.

There's a difference
between a philosophy and
a bumper sticker!

Never share your pad
with a restless bird!

It's impossible to be gloomy
when you're sitting
behind a marshmallow.

Try to avoid
long good-byes.

Feet should stay awake
in case you have to go
some place in a hurry!

I would have won,
but I got off to a bad finish!

It's all right to look interested,
but looking bored
is easier on the eyes ...

The early bird need not
pursue the worm when he can
order pizza at midnight.

The only time a dog
gets complimented is
when he doesn't do anything.

If your life is going by
too fast, maybe someone
pushed the fast-forward button.

Life is like a
ten-speed bicycle.
Most of us have
gears we never use.

Eating in the rain tends
to cool down your pizza.

You can't eat compliments.

Fat is not mature.

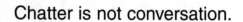

Chatter is not conversation.

He who lives by the dirty rotten little drop shot, dies by the dirty rotten little drop shot!

They say we all have to
deal with the law from
the very day we're born ...
so sue a baby!

Never complain about
the weather ... Whimper,
but don't complain.

Most of us have to be
satisfied if we just
look good at a distance.

When you leave for the afternoon, be careful how your secretary signs your letters.

S/w
(Dictated, but not
worth reading)

It's not difficult to find
your way in the wilderness if
you remember that Hollywood is
in the West and the moon
is always over Hollywood.

Decorate your home.
It gives the illusion that
your life is more interesting
than it really is.

A Christmas story should always have a character in it whom everyone can love.

Tiny Jim

What's good about hiking is there's no "offside".

If you're busy, you don't have to answer the phone, and sleeping is busy.

The sins of the stomach
are visited unto the body.

Be thankful and drink
a toast to the man who
invented the roof.

No matter how hard you try,
you can't steer a dog dish!

Never ask your secretary
to read something back.

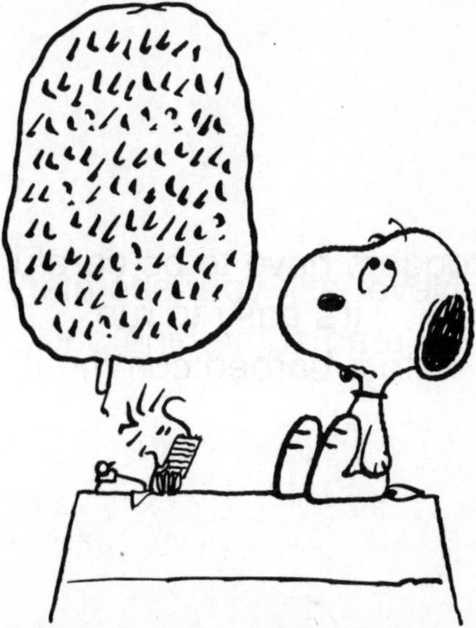

Joggers have to be careful –
it's easy to run
into a barbed comment!

Never neglect writing letters of appreciation to someone who has been good to you.

Other books available in this series ...
@ £2.50 each

Charlie Brown's Little Book of Wisdom
ISBN: 1 84161 099 2

Lucy's Little Book of Advice
ISBN: 1 84161 101 8

Peppermint Patty's Little Book of Blunders
ISBN: 1 84161 102 6

ℛℛ

RAVETTE PUBLISHING
Unit 3, Tristar Centre, Star Road, Partridge Green,
West Sussex RH13 8RA

Dear Supper Dish,